Co

570

FRIENDS
OF ACPL

3 1833 00747 5657

Little Boy Blue

FINGER PLAYS OLD AND NEW

by **Daphne Hogstrom**

illustrated by **Alice Schlesinger**

GOLDEN PRESS

Western Publishing Company, Inc.
Racine, Wisconsin

© 1966 by Western Publishing Company, Inc.

All rights reserved. Produced in U.S.A.

GOLDEN, A GOLDEN BOOK®, and GOLDEN PRESS® are
trademarks of Western Publishing Company, Inc. No part of
this book may be reproduced or copied in any form without
written permission from the publisher.

CO. SCHOOLS
C848795

LITTLE BOY BLUE

Little boy blue,
Come blow your horn,
The sheep's in the meadow,
The cow's in the corn!
Where is the boy who looks
    after the sheep?
He's under the haystack
    fast asleep.

Beckon. 1.
Blow horn. 2.
3. Point to right.
4. Point to left.
5. Raise arms questioningly.
6. Sleep.

THREE BLIND MICE

Three blind mice,
Three blind mice,
See how they run,
See how they run.

1.
Cover
eyes.

2.
Shade
eyes.

They all ran after
    the farmer's wife.
She cut off their tails
    with a carving knife.
Did you ever see such
    a sight in your life
As three blind mice!

3. Running motions with fingers.

4. Swooping, cutting motion.

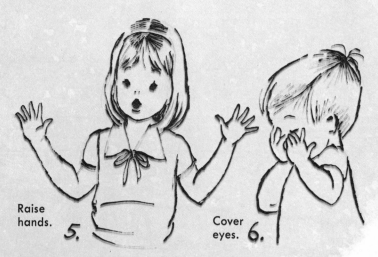

Raise hands. 5.

Cover eyes. 6.

ROW, ROW, ROW

Row, row, row your boat
Gently down the stream.
Merrily, merrily,
    merrily, merrily,
Life is but a dream.

1. Rowing motion, both hands.
2. Forward waving motion, one hand.
3. Clap hands.
4. Sleep.

THE SCARECROW

The scarecrow stands
With hanging hands
Beside the farmer's stile.
He scares the jay
And crow away
With just a painted smile.

1. Child stands.
2. Outstretched arms, hands hang limply.
3. Step in place.
4. Arms outstretched.
5. Add a happy, wide grin.

TWO LITTLE PUPPETS

Two little puppets,
One on each hand.
Isn't *she* pretty?
Isn't *he* grand?
Her name is Bella,
His name is Beau.
Hear *her* say,
   "Good morning."
Hear *him* say,
   "Hello!"

1. Hold up hands.
Each hand bobs.

2. Look toward right hand, wave fingers.

3. Look toward left hand, wave fingers.

4. Wave fingers of right hand.

5. Wave fingers of left hand.

6. Use high, squeaky voice. Bend hand in curtsey.

7. Use deep voice. Bend hand in bow.

FIVE LITTLE BABIES

One little baby
Rocking in a tree.
Two little babies
Splashing in the sea.
Three little babies
Crawling on the floor.
Four little babies
Banging on the door.
Five little babies
Playing hide-and-seek.
Keep your eyes
    closed tight, now,
Until I say . . .
    PEEK!

1. One finger.

2. Rocking motion with arms and hands.

3. Two fingers.

4. Splashing motion.

5. Three fingers.

6. Crawling motion with hands and arms.

7. Four fingers.

8. Pounding motion with fists.

9. Five fingers.

10. Cover eyes and peek.

AROUND AND ABOUT

Around and about,
Around and about,
Over and under
And in and out.
Run through the meadow,
Swim in the sea,
Slide down a mountain,
Climb up a tree!

1. Circular motion of index finger.

2. Swooping over-and-under motions with hand.

3. Wriggling in-and-out motions with hand.

4. Running motion, either hands or feet.

5. Swimming motion, hands and arms.

6. Sliding motion with hand.

7. Climbing motion, hands move upward above each other.

BOOM, BANG!

Boom, bang, boom, bang!
Rumpety, lumpety, bump!
Zoom, zam, zoom, zam!
Clippety, clappety, clump!
Rustles and bustles
    and swishes and zings —
What wonderful noises
    a thunderstorm brings!

1. Bang gong.

2. Beat drum.

3. Cut back and forth with alternate hands.

Clap hands louder and louder.
4.

Nod head from side to side in rhythm with words.
5.

6. Hug shoulders, rock in rhythm.

DIG A LITTLE HOLE

Dig a little hole,
Plant a little seed,
Pour a little water,
Pull a little weed.

1. Dig.

2. Drop seed.

Pour.

3.

4. Pull up and throw away.

Chase a little bug —
Heigh-ho, there he goes!
Give a little sunshine,
Grow a little rose.

5. Chasing motions with hands.

6. Shade eyes.

7. Cup hands, lift to the sun.

8. Smell flower, eyes closed, smiling.

PUDDLE MAGIC

The trees and sky are
    overhead
Until the raindrops fall.
Then trees and sky are
    underfoot
And, oh! I feel so tall!

1. Point upward.

2. Flutter fingers.

3. Point downward.

4. Stand tiptoe, stretch
upward, look up.

So splash along in puddles
And then just wait and see.
You'll walk among
    the treetops, too,
And feel sky-high, like me.

5. Kicking, splashing
motions of feet.

6. Finger lifted in a
wait-and-see motion.

7. Point to partner.

8. Stand tiptoe, stretch
upward.

LET'S BUILD A SNOWMAN

First the body
And then the head.
A stovepipe hat
And a scarf of red.
Pebbles for eyes,
And a carroty nose,
And a mouth made
   of raisins
In two smiling rows.

1. Stoop. Hold arms in big ball-shape.

2. Place smaller ball on top of first ball.

3. Place hat on head.

Wind imaginary scarf around neck.

4.

5. Place pebbles.

6. Place carrots.

7. Place raisins in rhythm with words.

OVER THE HILLS

Over the hills and far away
We skip and run and laugh
    and play.
Smell the flowers
    and fish the streams,
Lie in the sunshine
    and dream sweet dreams.

1. Bounding motion of hands.

2. Clap hands.

3. Sniff a flower.

4. Cast a fishing line.

5. Sleep, cheek resting on hand.

TWO LITTLE DICKYBIRDS

Two little dickybirds
Sitting on a wall —
One named Peter,
One named Paul.
Fly away, Peter.
Fly away, Paul.
Come back, Peter!
Come back, Paul!

1. Rest index fingers on table.

2. Lift and replace right finger.

3. Lift and replace left finger.

4. "Fly" right index finger over shoulder and change to middle finger.

5. Repeat with left hand.

6. "Fly" right hand over shoulder, change back to index finger.

7. Repeat with left hand.

ONE, TWO, BUCKLE MY SHOE

One, two, buckle my shoe,
Three, four, knock at the door,
Five, six, pick up sticks,
Seven, eight, lay them straight,
Nine, ten — a big, fat hen!

1. Buckle shoe.

Knock. 2.

3. Pick up sticks.

4. Lay sticks in a row.

Puff out chest, pull in chin, 5.
hold arms out and curved
at sides for wings.

GOING SHOPPING

Come to the store with me,
Just down the street.
We don't need a car,
We can go on our feet.
I have to buy cherries
And apples and steak,
Bread and bananas
And strawberry cake!

1. Beckon.
2. Point.
3. Pantomime steering a car.
4. Tap feet in place.
5. Pantomime small circles with fingers.
6. Pantomime big circle for apples, bigger circle for steak.
7. Pantomime long shapes for bread and bananas.
8. Rub tummy, smack lips.

IF

If I were a horse —
I'd neigh, of course!
If I were a bug,
I'd curl up in a rug!
If I were a bear,
I'd comb my hair!
If I were a pig,
I'd ride in a gig!
If I were a hen,
I'd scratch in my pen!
If I were a lynx,
I'd sit like a sphinx!
If I were a snail,
I'd crawl on the trail!
But if I were a gnu —
I'd have nothing to do!

1. Fingers for ears. Neigh the word "neigh."

2. Cup hands.

3. Hug self.

4. Hold hands like paws.

5. Comb hair all over body.

6. Puff cheeks.

7. Hold reins, jog.

8. Flap arms.

9. Scratch ground.

10. Touch "whiskers."

11. Hold arms stiffly forward at waist height, hold head stiff and close eyes.

12. Raise arms in roof shape. Crawling motion of fingers.

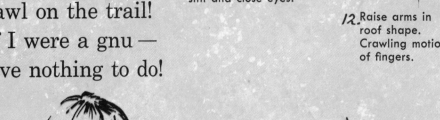

Raise hands. Shrug shoulders.

Fingers for horns.

14.

13.

ALL THE SEAS

If all the seas
were one sea,
What a GREAT sea
that would be!
If all the trees
were one tree,
What a GREAT tree
that would be!

Arms wide. *1.*

Hands
raised. *2.*

3.

Look up.
Shade eyes.

Hands raised
in amazement.
4.

If all the axes
 were one axe,
What a GREAT axe
 that would be!
And if all the men
 were one man,
What a GREAT man
 that would be!

Measure axe. 5.

Hands
raised. 6.

Measure
man. 7.

Hands raised
in amazement. 8.

And if the great MAN
Took the great AXE
And chopped down
 the great TREE
And it fell into
 the great SEA—
What a great SPLASH!
 that would be!

Repeat actions 1 through 8.
Lift arms high on "Splash."